Contents

Introduction

This Little Book offers practitioners ideas for simple maths activities and games for children in the Early Years Foundation Stage. All the activities make use of materials and equipment which are readily found in most settings, or can be bought easily and cheaply.

Most of the activities need little or no preparation, but some need you to collect items or prepare materials yourself or with the children before you start. In these cases instructions are included, and there is a selection of photocopiable resources at the end of the book.

Early mathematical learning

Mathematical learning throughout the Early Years Foundation Stage must be rooted in firsthand, practical activities. The guidance documents from the QCA and the National Numeracy Strategy are united in stating that 'practitioners should give particular attention to: practical activities that are imaginative and enjoyable'. (QCA Guidance 2000).

'Lessons will often include, or be based upon, well planned opportunities for children's play. Examples of these will be found in the QCA/DfES document Curriculum Guidance for the Foundation Stage.' (Guidance for Mathematics in Reception Classes, NNS 2000).

Links with the goals for the Early Years Foundation Stage

The QCA Guidance for the Foundation Stage recommends: 'many different activities, some of which will focus on mathematical development, and some of which will draw on mathematical learning in other activities.'

Activities in the Early Years Foundation Stage have many applications. Numbers, shapes, counting and measuring, all feature in familiar activities throughout the day and with children of all ages and stages of development.

At first children need lots of opportunities for free access to mathematical apparatus, experimenting and exploring the equipment through play. This need for free play with apparatus continues throughout the Early Years Foundation Stage, and well into Key Stage 1.

However, as children develop they need the support of adults in their learning, if they are to make the best possible progress towards the Early Learning Goals. Sometimes, an activity or discussion may be planned and initiated by an adult, to provide a new experience, to introduce specific vocabulary, or to support and extend a particular stage of development.

At other times, the children will become involved in mathematical thinking during play which they have initiated themselves – counting, sorting, experimenting with language, on their own, in groups or with the support of an adult – practising, consolidating and refining their learning. Children need plenty of both sorts of experience throughout the Foundation Stage.

Mathematical activities and games, in adult or child initiated situations, can give opportunities for learning in all areas of learning. For example, in:

Problem solving, reasoning and numeracy

▶ say and use number names in order in familiar contexts

▶ count reliably up to 10 everyday objects

▶ recognise numerals 1–9

▶ use developing mathematical ideas and methods to solve practical problems

▶ in practical activities and discussion begin to use the vocabulary involved in addition and subtraction

▶ use language such as more, less, to compare two numbers

▶ find one more or one less than a number from 1–10

▶ begin to relate addition to combining two groups of objects, and subtraction to taking away

▶ use language such as greater, smaller, heavier or lighter to compare quantities

▶ use everyday words to describe position

▶ talk about, recognise and recreate simple patterns

- ▶ use developing mathematical ideas and methods to solve practical problems.

...and of course, there are many and varied opportunities to develop mathematical concepts in the other areas of experience.

Communication, language and literacy

- ▶ interact with others, negotiating plans and activities and taking turns
- ▶ extend their vocabulary, exploring the meanings and sounds of new words
- ▶ listen to stories, rhymes and songs

Personal, social and emotional development

- ▶ be confident to try new activities, initiate ideas and speak in a familiar group
- ▶ work as part of a group or class, taking turns and sharing fairly
- ▶ select and use activities and resources independently.

Promoting mathematical thinking

If children are to reach the mathematical goals for learning, they must start with extensive practical experience of mathematics in language; in song, rhyme and story; in creative work, construction, sand, water and cooking. Mathematical language and thinking must be as apparent outside as it is indoors, as common as our reference to and value for books and spoken language.

Children need access to mathematical equipment, language and thinking in free play before consolidating concepts in adult led activities.
Practitioners can be influential in this process by:

- ▶ providing activities and resources that promote mathematical thinking, and modelling mathematical thinking yourselves
- ▶ using mathematical language in discussions, conversations and interactions with children
- ▶ giving children access to materials such as number cards, counting and measuring apparatus, multiples of objects, etc. to select from in free play

- using a variety of counting songs, rhymes and stories to reinforce language and thinking (remember the power of movement and music in memory and recall!)
- exploring the opportunities of role-play and outside play in developing mathematical learning
- encouraging problem solving attitudes from the earliest age.

How this book works

Each of the pages in the book contains ideas for using a resource in a range of play and exploration situations, and ideas for experiences leading to each of the clusters or aspects of learning within mathematical development.

The clusters or aspects of learning within mathematics are:

1. Numbers as labels for counting
2. Calculating
3. Shape, space and measures

Each page covers free play ideas, as well as all clusters:

- double page spreads have separate sections for each cluster
- single pages have a range of activities in a more general form.

A number walk

Number walks are a good way of exploring number in the local environment, either in your setting or in the neighbourhood.

Make sure you talk to the children before you leave, emphasising that you are looking for numbers, shapes and symbols. Take some clipboards, pens and a camera, so you can record what you see. You could use the photos to make a counting book of people, things or numbers you have seen – e.g. one policeman, two babies, three postboxes, four lorries, five dogs. You could also make a book of shapes you have seen in the environment.

If you can build in some shopping, you will be able to do even more on your mathematical walk – lists, money, change, prices, counting, weighing.

Number walks for free play situations

▶ Encourage children to look and notice numbers, shapes and symbols in daily activities and the life of your setting.

▶ Talk about numbers, symbols and signs in reading, shopping, registers, children absent, drinks and snacks, etc.

▶ Talk about numbers, dates, days, etc.

▶ Make sure numbers are just as frequently displayed as letters, make number signs, directions, arrows, door numbers, etc.

Numbers as labels and for counting

▶ Count the number of steps to a corner, along a path, to a shop.

▶ Tally or put a counter in a tin every time you see a dog, a baby, a bird, a postbox.

▶ Look for house numbers, street signs with mileage, petrol pumps and cars with numbers, prices in shops, phone numbers on vans or lorries.

▶ Use your camera to snap numbers, objects and people.

Calculating

▶ Use the photos you take to talk about more and less. Take some photos of objects for a one more/one less card game. Make some photos into cards for ordering and counting.

▶ Look at numbers on houses and street signs, and talk about further, nearer, more and less.

▶ Visit shops or market stalls. Buy some things and work out totals and change.

▶ Make guesses (early estimation), e.g. 'Are there more oranges or apples?'

Shape, space and measures

▶ Spot shapes, signs, symbols as you walk.

▶ Look for directions and instructions, arrows, street signs, roundabouts etc.

▶ Visit shops or markets and spot prices, cash registers, scales and balances.

▶ Find clocks, both analogue and digital, and track the time.

Children's fingers, hands and feet

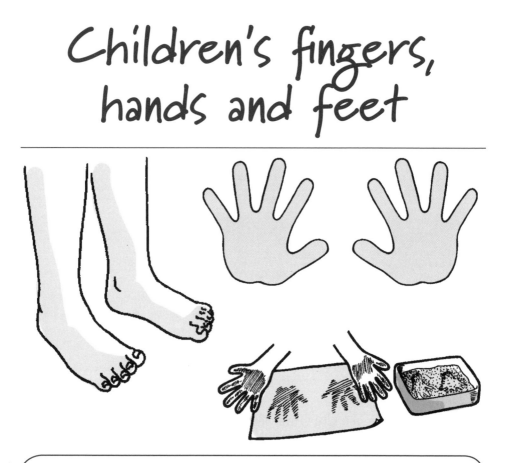

Children's fingers and hands are the counting apparatus that is always with them. Practitioners are always aware of the importance of developing fluency with finger games, songs and rhymes as soon as possible. A good repertoire of these games is an essential tool for mathematical work in the Foundation Stage, and we have included a few of these games on the next page. You will find some more songs on page 61.

Children also need a good sense of rhythm if they are to succeed in reading and writing activities, so we need to strengthen the fine motor muscles of hands, feet, wrists, and ankles. Using both hands to trace, draw, paint, clap and slap will reinforce the learning. Singing and chanting words, stamping, hopping and jumping will also help memory and recall.

Using finger games in free play situations

▶ Use some of the songs and rhymes on page 61 to develop number awareness and fine motor control.

▶ Record some finger rhymes.

▶ Any activity with little pieces or items such as puzzles, pegs, paper clips, coins, etc. will help with finger movement and control. Thread beads, use feely bags, pick up small objects.

▶ Walk along lines, balancing, jumping, climbing and hopping.

Numbers as labels and for counting

▶ Make finger and hand prints with stamp pads or paint.

▶ Play quick games of 'Show four fingers', 'Show three fingers'. Say the number or hold up a number card.

▶ Songs like Two Little Dicky Birds, Five Little Frogs, Five Fat Sausages, Ten Green Bottles, holding up the right number of fingers.

▶ Use fingers to walk along number lines and up number ladders.

▶ Clap and count to rhymes and songs, clap your name.

Calculating

▶ Play 'Hold up one finger, hold up one more,' ' Hold up four fingers, now one less'.

▶ Walk fingers up and down number lines, one more, one less.

▶ Put dry pasta shapes in a bag – 'Take one more than five', 'Take one less than three'.

▶ Play 'Echo' – clapping, drumming, slapping, stamping a number and children clap etc back one more or one less.

▶ Use number cards. Turn over two at a time and clap the total.

Shape, space and measures

▶ Use fingers to draw numbers, shapes in the air, on the floor, on each others' backs.

▶ Put on blindfolds – then feel small objects, other children's faces, shapes or plastic numbers, and guess what or who they are.

▶ Make repeating sound patterns with slaps, claps, jumps and other body music.

Children's bodies

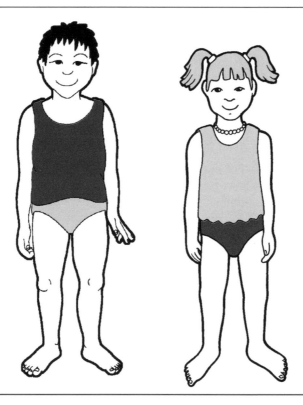

Whole body learning is learning that stays! Make sure your children learn with the whole of their bodies whenever they can. We now know that children will learn only 30% of what they see, but nearer 90% of what they see, say and do at the same time! If you can add singing, rhythmic work, rhyme and music, they will learn even more.

Outside space also gives an opportunity for children to understand the language of space and direction – feeling the words of size, shape, direction and position with their whole bodies will make the concepts easier to understand and will reinforce memory and recall.

Use some of these ideas outside or in the hall if you haven't got space in your room.

Using whole bodies in free play situations

▶ Give them plenty of opportunities to move, both indoors and out, with and without apparatus or equipment.

▶ Use informal opportunities to talk about parts of the body, movements and positions.

▶ Talk informally about similarities and differences in people, animals, things, likes and dislikes. Encourage use of all their limbs and parts of the body when playing.

Numbers as labels and for counting

▶ Play whole body race games on snakes and ladders or number lines chalked on the ground or made with masking tape on the floor.

▶ Clap and stamp and jump names, words and numbers.

▶ Play hopscotch and other playground games.

▶ Sing 'Heads, Shoulders, Knees and Toes' and other 'body songs' to develop listening skills.

▶ Use a drum or tambourine for counting practice, attentive listening, following patterns and beats.

Calculating

Using the children themselves to help with understanding of groups and grouping, joining groups and adding more.

▶ Use hoops, playground chalk or ropes to make circles for counting sets of children. Then try joining and dividing sets to give whole body understanding of addition and subtraction.

▶ Use your giant number lines or ladders chalked or painted on the ground to practise counting on and back (don't forget to add 0 to your lines).

Shape, space and measures

▶ Use the children themselves to sort according to hair colour, gender, age.

▶ Help the children to order themselves in height, hair length, shoe size etc. Make simple bar charts with Unifix cubes etc.

▶ Use whole body movement to help with the development of a sense of space, direction and position. Use climbing apparatus, or outside space to talk about 'under, through, over, up, along.'

Compare bears

Compare Bears come in sets with several different sizes and colours. They are useful materials for sorting and ordering sets and collections, and talking about position, particularly because they can be used for the teaching of a range of concepts.

However, if you don't have a special set, you can use any materials that come in different sizes and colours e.g. Lego bricks, counters, wooden bricks, Stickle Bricks etc. You could also make your own sets of objects with dough (coloured with paint or food colouring), baked and varnished.

Sorting, ordering and grading can also be done with common objects (length with ribbon or string, size with potatoes or pebbles, colour with crayons, paper clips, or pegs).

Using Compare Bears in free play

▶ Make the bears or other 'family sets' of creatures available for free play with bricks or other construction sets.

▶ Leave some near the sand or water.

▶ Leave a box on the maths table or shelf for free play in sorting, ordering or playing.

▶ Use the bears to illustrate stories such as 'The Three Bears', 'A Bear Hunt', 'Peace at Last'.

Numbers as labels and for counting

▶ Use bears of the same size, and line them up for counting and labelling with number labels.

▶ Use bears of the same size and sort them according to colour.

▶ Use bears of all sizes and sort them according to colour or size.

▶ Use bears of all sizes and put them in 'families' a big, medium and small in each family.

▶ Put a bunch of bears in a feely bag and find a small one, a big one, a medium one.

Calculating

▶ Find three red bears, then one more, one less.

▶ Find three big bears, put back one, how many now?

▶ Play 'Race to the Cottage'. Use the race game on pages 50–51 or make your own game on a piece of card. Make some cards that say 'Go on one', 'Go back one' (or Go on two, Go back two). Each player starts with a bear at the beginning of the path through the woods. Take turns to turn over a card and move forward or back. The first player to the cottage wins.

Shape, space and measures

▶ Use Compare Bears or other materials to practise the language of size (big, bigger, biggest; small, smaller, smallest; tall/short).

▶ Use Compare Bears or other materials for balance and weighing. Talk with the children as they work, about the concepts of smaller/lighter, bigger/heavier. Using Compare Bears or other identical items introduces standard units for measuring.

Using small bricks

Make matching games

Use small bricks and paint to help the children make their own number games. Print different numbers and patterns of bricks on cards, and use them to count, match, play Snap or pairs. Make some number cards too.

Build towers and count them

Use bricks to build towers outside. Label them with number cards and labels. Use bricks and large blocks to make structures and enclosures. Look at the way brick walls are made to be strong.

Sort

Use collections of bricks to sort for shape, size or colour, number of corners or faces. Collect bricks inside hoops or chalk circles.

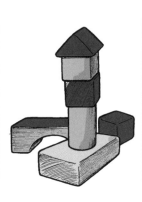

Feel it

Make a feely bag and fill it with bricks. Feel a brick, name it and then look, or follow instructions to find a brick by feeling.

Play

Play 'Find the shape'. Choose a brick or block and find or say something that is the same shape. e.g. a rectangular brick is like a box or a book; a cylindrical brick is like a pen or a mug; a square brick is like a sugar cube.

Make and find patterns

Make matching or repeating patterns with colours or shapes. Look for patterns in walls and other brick structures. Use bricks to print patterns on paper or on the ground.

Using hoops, balls, ropes, and cones

Play scoring games

Play scoring games with balls, quoits or bean bags. Draw targets, tracks or starting lines on the wall or ground with playground chalk. Use small whiteboards or blackboards for scoring. Put up some simple goals for football.

Sort the children

Sort the children into different sets – e.g. boys/girls; long/short hair; shoe colour; age. Collect the different sets of children inside hoops, in ropes or in circles chalked on the ground.

Make skittles

Fill empty plastic bottles with sand or gravel, stick a number on each and play with a soft ball.

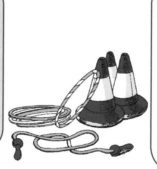

Race games

Mark some simple tracks for racing (children or toy cars). Use these to learn about first, second, third etc.

Play Hoop Jump

Put some different coloured hoops on the ground (on the grass is best). Call a colour and the children must run to the right hoop. Change the fun by asking them to jump, hop, crawl, walk backwards or jump from hoop to hoop.

Play ball games

Find a really big box and cut holes in the sides. Mark each hole with a score from 1 to 3 and make a scoring game by throwing small balls in the numbered holes. A child can get inside the box to fetch the balls out again!

Dice and spinners

Dice and spinners come in many shapes, sizes and types.

Collect a variety, and try to include:

▶ different sizes – from board game dice to big floor dice

▶ different materials – plastic, card, sponge, wood, fabric

▶ different types – picture, dotty, shape, number, money. It's quite easy to make your own from squares of sponge, card or wooden blocks.

Any box with six surfaces can be a dice – stock cube boxes, cube tissue boxes etc. Cover or paint them if you like, then add stickers with numbers, pictures, dots or shapes. Small dice are easier to control if they are captured in a little jar or clear box. Put on the lid and simply shake the jar to score.

Using dice and spinners in free play

▶ Make sure there are dice and spinners in your maths area for free play.

▶ Put a dice game in the home corner cupboard, in the quiet area or on a table. Suggest that adult helpers play games with children who choose to join in.

▶ Make or buy some giant outdoor dice in foam or plastic, and play some outdooor dice games.

Numbers as labels and for counting

Use either a dotty or a number dice or spinner:

▶ Roll the dice or spinner, say the number.

▶ Roll the dice or spinner, take the right number of counters.

▶ Roll the dice or spinner, find the number on a line.

▶ Roll the dice, jump, hop, clap or stand and sit to match the number.

▶ Roll the dice or spinner, place shells in a tin, cars in a basket.

▶ Draw a ladder each, roll the dice, move up the ladder. (see template on page 48)

Calculating

Use stickers to make some dice with numbers or dots– 1 and 2 only; 1, 2 and 3 only; 1, 2, 3 and 4; or 1 to 5:

▶ Roll a dice or spinner, say the number, then say the number which is one more or one less.

▶ Roll the dice or spinner, find the number on a number line, then say the number which is one more/one less.

▶ Roll the dice or spinner and use counters to play – 'Give me one more/two more/three more'.

▶ Roll two dotty dice or spinners – say how many altogether.

Shape, space and measures

▶ Roll a shape dice or spinner, draw the shape in the air or name it.

▶ Roll a shape dice, say the name of something the same shape.

▶ Roll a money dice, pick the coin from a collection of real coins.

▶ Make shape bingo - look on pages 46 – 47 for instructions for Bingo games. The caller rolls the dice or spinner and names the shape. Players cover that shape with a counter or blank card.

Dominoes

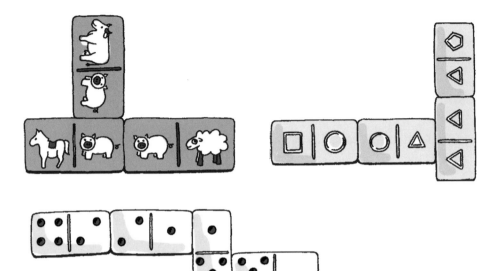

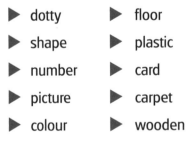

Dominoes come in many sorts and sizes. Try to collect some of the following:

- ▶ dotty
- ▶ shape
- ▶ number
- ▶ picture
- ▶ colour

- ▶ floor
- ▶ plastic
- ▶ card
- ▶ carpet
- ▶ wooden

You can mix sets for additional fun and more mathematical experience. You can also make dominoes from wrapping paper, digital photos, stamps, sticky shapes, children's pictures (reduced and duplicated on a photocopier). Stick on card and laminate. Add numbers, dots, stars, etc. for counting.

Using dominoes in free play situations

▶ Offer dominoes as a free choice activity for pairs or groups.

▶ Make some giant dominoes from sponge, plastic sheet or carpet. Use them outdoors for giant games on paths or grass.

▶ Make some domino blanks from card and offer them in the creative or maths area with stickers or picture stamps, so the children can make and play their own versions.

Numbers as labels and for counting

▶ Pick a dotty domino and count the spots. Then pick a number card to match. Keep it if you are right.

▶ Use two sets to match numbers with pictures or dots.

▶ Group dominoes with the same number, picture, shape.

▶ Spread out dominoes – first to find a domino with five spots, four dogs etc.

▶ Take three dominoes. Put a number label by each end.

Calculating

▶ Play domino pairs. Place dotty or number dominoes face down. Turn over two. If they have the same total keep them, if not, turn them back.

▶ Join dominoes in any order – say the total each time.

▶ Put dominoes in a feely bag. Put in hand, say the number of dots. If you are right, keep the domino, if not, put it back.

▶ Find a domino with two more than five, one less than six, four more than one.

Shape, space and measures

▶ Play shape dominoes.

▶ Make or buy money dominoes and play games.

▶ Mix money and dot dominoes for a new dominoes game.

▶ Collect a selection of dominoes and use to answer problems such as: 'A domino with a three sided shape', 'Three dominoes, each with seven spots', 'Two dominoes with a total of 10 dots.'

Using small objects

(e.g. paper clips, pegs, elastic bands, coins, beads, beans, buttons, pasta)

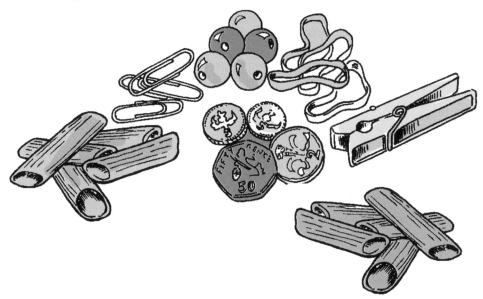

These games and activities involve children in using small items, and developing their fine motor control while they learn about numbers. Using a range of different items is a good experience. We often give children identical items to count but variety will help them to consolidate number knowledge and recognition.

Spreading the items out in different patterns also helps with learning. Making patterns and pictures with familiar objects is also an interesting way to explore shape and space. Filling and emptying, mixing and sorting, putting items in bags, making shops and pretending to cook, weigh and measure all develop familiarity with measure, money and counting. The small items are inexpensive and encourage extension in counting.

Using small items in free play situations

▶ Set up a shop for free play inside or out. Offer bags, plastic jars, scales, note pads, card for prices, sorting trays, etc. and let them set up their own shop.

▶ Provide plastic jars of small items for free sorting, mixing, etc.

▶ Boxes with slots and holes of various sizes and shapes, funnels, scoops and ladles, tweezers and tongs will all help with fine motor control. Encourage them to count as they scoop or post.

Numbers as labels and for counting

Collect some bowls, food trays or plastic jars of small items and label them with pictures and words.

▶ Put out lines of identical objects; count and label them.

▶ Put out lines of mixed objects, or patterns of objects to count.

▶ Concentrate on one number (say five) and see how many different patterns you can make with five objects.

▶ Mix the objects with sand and then sift them out.

▶ Grab a handful, guess how many, then count.

Calculating

▶ Play 'One More' – take a few, count, then take one more. Play the same game with 'One Less'.

▶ Join and separate small groups of objects on paper plates, in cups or on paper circles to make simple addition and subtraction challenges.

▶ Use number cards (small numbers at first) to play a game where they take turns to turn over a card and take that number of objects. Try adding each time.

Shape, space and measures

▶ Fill small plastic or paper bags with objects and make a shop. Use real coins to buy and sell 1p, 2p, 3p bags.

▶ Use the objects to fill containers, boxes, cups.

▶ Offer balance scales for experimentation with small objects.

▶ Use linked paper clips to measure – an early way of using standard units.

Money (plastic or real)

Children love playing with money – plastic, card or real. Real coins are always best, but children do need to practise looking after them! You could start by storing the coins in groups of five in an egg box – easy for them to check in and check out.

Most children will have had some experience of coins, but may not have consolidated their knowledge of how coins work. It sometimes takes a long time for them to realise that a 2p coin is worth twice as much as a 1p coin and that the small 5p coin is worth five times as much as the larger 1p. With this in mind, it would be helpful to their learning to start with small denominations – just pennies at first, adding 2p and 5p coins when they have had experience of exchanging 1 for 1.
(There are coins for copying on page 48.)

Using coins in free play situations

▶ Make sure there are coins (real or plastic) in your maths area.

▶ Add plastic or real money and wallets, purses, bags and baskets to role-play situations, encourage the making of tickets and labels, paying for services such as car washing, using tills, etc.

▶ Try to take children with you to shop for snacks, fruit, cooking ingredients. Make lists, count out money, talk about change.

Numbers as labels and for counting

▶ Put some coins in a feely bag and try to guess which coin is which by touch alone.

▶ Use pennies and number cards to match and count.

▶ Make a coin recognition Bingo game. Put coins on the playing boards and numbers on the cards (start with just pennies).

▶ Make a Snap or Pairs game with coin stamps, sticky coins or coin rubbings.

▶ Make some money dominoes.

Calculating

▶ Put some coins in two feely bags. Take a coin from each bag and say how much there is altogether.

▶ Giving change is a very good subtracting exercise. When children can use 1p, 2p, 5p and 10p coins, play a game that involves the giving of change. Collect up some toys, make price labels and show them how change works. Use real coins if you can.

▶ Put some coins (1p, 2p, 5p) in a feely bag. Pull one out and say how many more to make 10p.

Shape, space and measures

▶ Make a shopping game with pictures from a catalogue. Stick the pictures on cards and add a price in numbers. Use real or plastic money to pay for the things.

▶ Try a probability game. You need two ladder cards (page 49). Take turns to toss a coin. Toss heads, go up one, toss tails, go down one. First to the top wins.

Using coloured counters

Sort and count

Use counters to sort and count in sorting trays, little hoops, circles drawn on paper, large elastic bands. Sort by colour, size, shape. Label the sets with number labels or cards.

Play a game

Use counters to play Tiddly Winks. Mark some small circles on paper or card. Write a score in each. Now take turns to flip the counters into the circle. Use a white board to collect the scores and find the winner.

Bag them

Find some small zip-lock bags and fill and label each with a different number or colour of counters. Label the bags.

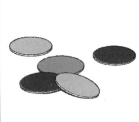

ICT

Use a drawing programme to make counters for matching games and cards. Print and stick on card or laminate.

Patterns

Make some matching pattern cards by drawing round counters or using sticky paper dots or circles. Match with counters. Make another set with numbers and no counters to put the right number of counters on.

Stick them down

Use a glue gun (adult only!) to stick some counters to cards for a tactile domino game, pairs game or for your feely bag. Make pictures for matching cards.

Beads and strings

Sort and count

Offer beads and strings as a choice on a maths table or shelf. Make sure there are several different sizes, types and colours for sorting. For older ones, add some number labels with holes in. Store in clear jars.

Threading

Threading is good for helping fine motor control and eye/hand coordination. Make sure the laces have a knot in the end to avoid frustration, and that they have firm ends for threading. Offer several lengths.

Bead threaders

Dip the end of wool or thin string in melted candle wax. Leave to harden and it will make threading easier.

A Game

Each player has a string. Toss a dice and thread the number of beads. First to have 20 beads on their string wins.

Pattern cards

Make some pattern cards for children to copy. Draw and colour the beads in sequences. Start with colour only sequences, then shape only, then size only, then colour and size or shape. Keep all three for the oldest children.

A threading game

Each player has a string. Make about 20 'add 1', 'take 1' cards (with beads and words). Take turns to take a card and add or take beads from your string. The winner is the first to get 5 or 10 beads on their string.

A floor number line

You could buy or make this sort of line. If you make it yourself, you can extend it as the children learn new numbers, or to differentiate it for children at different levels.

You need either a long thin piece of carpet or some carpet squares (ask your local carpet shop or parents if they have an offcut). A carpet line should be about 45cm (18") wide and about 3m (10 feet) long, so children can stand on the numbers. Measure and mark out, then paint or mark the numbers. Start at 0 and go up to 10 until children have mastered these numbers, then add more, sticking them on with carpet tape. If you use carpet tiles, use one for each number and stick them together on the back with carpet tape. This will make it fold up in a zigzag. If you have room you could stick the line to the floor or even to the ground outside.

Using number lines in free play situations

▶ Paint or chalk number lines, stepping stones, ladders or snakes (with or without numbers) outside, or make a line inside with masking tape.

▶ Play hopscotch and other ladder games outside or in the hall.

▶ Make some simple race games for children to play on their own with dice or spinners. Use cars or big counters as playing pieces. Offer children these outside on a rug or carpet sample.

Numbers as labels and for counting

▶ Walk, jump, hop and count, forwards and backwards.

▶ Find a soft toy or car each, use a floor dice to toss and race along the line.

▶ Use small objects. Put the right number on each square.

▶ Make some cards that say 'move on 1', 'move on 2', 'move back 1', etc. Start on zero, pick a card and move as it says. First to the end of the line wins.

▶ Put the numbers on carpet squares, jumble, then sort them.

Calculating

▶ Make the Frog Hopper Game (on pages 52–53) and play 'hop on, hop back on the lily pads'. It's even more fun if you use small toy frogs as game pieces.

▶ Make cards that say '1 more', '2 less', '4 more', etc. Start a marker or toy on zero, take turns to take a card and see who is the first to get to 10.

▶ Start at 10 and play 'count backwards' by throwing a dice or picking numbers from a bag.

▶ Throw two dice and race along the line, adding the numbers.

Shape, space and measures

▶ To give children a sense of space and position, use your number line to play 'Jump on, Jump back' with a homemade floor dice. Children get on the number line, someone throws the dice, the children move back and forward. This is terrific fun!

▶ You could also make giant versions of Snakes and Ladders, hundred squares, rockets with count down numbers, counting spirals, etc., with carpet tiles, paint or chalk.

A pack of playing cards

This resource is cheap to buy and is familiar to many children. Packs of cards also have many uses for learning. You can use the whole set for 'Pairs' and 'Snap' games, or remove the picture cards to use for number games.

Two or more sets will give you plenty of scope when you are working with limited numbers – say from 1 to 5. The different designs encourage close observation and generalisation of number concepts.

Many catalogues supply packs of blank playing cards for:

▶ making your own games

▶ adding zero

▶ adding numbers beyond 10

▶ making pictorial, dotty or pattern cards.

Using packs of cards in free play situations

▶ Put a pack in the home corner for games playing.

▶ Put a pack of cards and a blanket in a basket and offer for outdoor play.

▶ Offer card games ('Snap', 'Happy Families', matching or pairs games) as free choice activities or games to play with adults. These games will help them to practise taking turns and looking closely at individual cards as well as developing their memories.

Numbers as labels and for counting

▶ Spread the cards on a table, face up – play 'quickest to find.'

▶ Take five cards and put them in order (quickest wins).

▶ Play 'Snap' or 'Pairs'. Use the cards from 1 to 3 from each suit first (12 cards), then gradually add more.

▶ Sort and order part of a pack counting forwards or backwards.

▶ Use number labels to match with playing cards.

▶ Use a small number of cards (say six). Lay out in order, shuffle, remove a card, which one is missing?

Calculating (from green stepping stone level)

▶ Pick a card from pack or a bag, say one more/one less. If right, keep the card, if not, put it back.

▶ Turn over two or three cards and add the total.

▶ Play 'more' or 'less' Snap - turn over a card each, the player whose card is more/less wins both cards. Start with small values.

▶ Start with any card, find cards with two more, then two more, and two more.

▶ Roll two dice, find the card with the total dots. (You may want to explain about Jacks, Queens and Kings!)

Shape, space and measures

▶ Sort into sets by shape of suit.

▶ Use the cards as a standard unit for measuring.

▶ Draw round flat shapes or use sticky paper shapes to make some blank playing cards into a shape snap or pairs game.

▶ Stick paper or real coins on blank cards to use in the same way (a glue gun will stick coins to card), or copy the coins on page 48.

▶ Make a set of shape snap cards from blank playing cards.

Number cards and tiles

Make or buy several sets of these number cards/tiles. It is useful to have different sizes and colours of numerals, and multiples of each number. For the group activities, use cards that are at least 10cm (4") square, so everyone in the group can see the numbers. Younger children may need even bigger cards.

Start with numbers 1 to 5, then add 0, then gradually add the other numbers to 10 and beyond as the children develop their number knowledge.

N.B. Plastic cards will last longer, but they are not any better than ones you make yourself! Draw lines on a sheet of card, write the numbers with a thick marker, and laminate or seal with sticky backed plastic before you cut them up! Make some picture cards for matching and playing pairs.

Using number tiles in free play situations

▶ Offer number tiles as free access materials in your number area.

▶ Leave some number tiles or cards by the sand, bricks or construction area.

▶ Hang number cards by activities to indicate how many children may play there.

▶ Use number cards outside to number bikes and other toys.

Numbers as labels and for counting

▶ Set out a line of cars, bears or other objects. Use the cards to number them and count on and back.

▶ Put small numbers of objects (pegs, coins, counters, small toys) in zip-lock bags. Count and label with cards.

▶ Put small objects in a feely bag, grab some, count and choose a label.

▶ Bury some small items in the sand tray. Use aquarium nets or sieves to scoop the sand. Count the number of objects collected and choose the correct number label for your catch.

Calculating (from green stepping stone level)

▶ Pick two number cards and say how many altogether (start small!).

▶ Put out a group of objects, count, take some away and label what's left.

▶ Count two into a bag, box or tin, add more – how many now? Find the number.

▶ Put five toy cars in a box. Take out a few (perhaps two). How many left? Find the number.

▶ Play a fishing game and find the number one more or one less than your catch.

Shape, space and measures

▶ Line up flat shapes and use the cards to number them.

▶ Find the number card for the number of corners, sides or faces of a shape.

▶ Sort shapes into sets labelled with the number cards.

▶ Match number cards with different coins (to 10p).

▶ Use number cards with Bingo base cards to match numbers to numbers, numbers to pictures or dots, numbers to coins.

Dough, clay and cooking equipment

Dough and clay are ideal materials for maths work, and cooking can provide a wealth of enjoyable activities to support counting, calculating, shape, space and measures.

Children should be involved in the making of dough whenever possible – it is a simple and safe experience which children in many settings undertake independently, particularly where they have a pictorial recipe to follow and easily accessible ingredients.

Cooking is also an experience which gives opportunities to foster independence. Simple recipe books and a well organised cooking area all help adults and children to have regular experience of this enjoyable activity. Sharing the results is an added bonus!

Clay and cooking in free play situations

▶ Make cooking a regular event, and make sure the adults are all aware of the possibilities for number work in cooking.

▶ Make dough with the children. Find a recipe in spoons or cups for the youngest children, so they can count and measure for themselves.

▶ As children work with free play activities, talk with them, using the language of counting, shape, size, position.

Numbers as labels and for counting

▶ Make numbers from dough. Bake some to use as labels.

▶ Make dough into counters, beads, balls and use for counting, threading and sorting.

▶ Make playing pieces for games – make simple discs, flatten the pieces and stamp with animal shapes, or cut out with small shaped cutters. Bake, paint and then varnish with PVA glue to make them last longer. Make some big ones for floor number lines or outside games.

Calculating (from green stepping stone level)

▶ Begin by working with lumps of dough, dividing into different numbers of pieces and joining to make bigger pieces. Divide into half, quarters, share between two or three etc.

▶ Play 'Put and Take' with dough pieces or other objects. Make some cards that say 'Put 1', 'Take 1'. Each player starts with five dough counters (or other objects), and some go in the middle of the table. Take turns to turn over a card and put one in or take one from the centre of the table. The first one to collect 10 wins.

Shape, space and measures

▶ Make shapes with cutters.

▶ Look at patterns as you use cookie trays or jam tart tins.

▶ Practise weighing and counting with spoons and scales as you help them to cook or make dough for themselves.

▶ Take the children shopping whenever possible, to buy ingredients and use money.

Using junk mail and wrapping paper

Make a game

Collect several identical pieces of junk mail or catalogues or buy two sheets of wrapping paper. Use to make matching games. Help the children to cut out matching pictures, stick on card (old cereal boxes will do). Play snap or pairs.

Make lotto games

Use food junk mail/wrapping paper to collect pictures with multiple items – three bean cans, four babies, two Christmas trees, etc. Stick the pictures on the lotto boards and make some number cards for the caller.
(see pages 46 – 47)

Find numbers

Give the children a pile of junk mail and scissors or felt pens to find and cut out or circle numbers.

Play Spot It

This game speeds up eye movement and concentration. Use junk mail to play 'First to spot the shape, number, item, colour'.

Collect sets of things

Use junk mail, catalogues, free newspapers etc. to collect sets of food, vehicles, toys, things for rooms of a house, clothes, children. Make simple books and posters. Count and label simple collections with words and numbers.

Look for shapes

Use junk mail to make collections of colours, shapes and sizes of things, e.g. big cars and little cars, rectangular things, circles, red things, things with spots and stripes, things bigger than me.

Using containers

For measuring

Collect empty plastic containers for capacity work with sand, water, rice or lentils. Make sure you have plenty of sizes and some very small things. Encourage children to count aloud as they fill one container with another.

Sort and count

Collect plastic trays from fruit and vegetables (avoid those used for meat or fish). Use for sorting beads, shapes, small objects. Egg boxes make good sorting trays too. Number the spaces if the children are ready.

Captive dice

Put dice in small plastic jars or containers to stop them spinning off the table during games.

Zip-lock bags

Put collections of small items in little zip-lock bags for counting. Label them with number labels or small stickers.

Collecting things

Try a scavenger hunt. Give each child a food tray with dividers. Challenge them to collect a number of items in each space (from the room or outside). Start with the same number in each space, then try different or sequenced numbers.

Making timers

Use plastic bottles. Fill with sand, put lid back, make a hole in the lid and turn upside down. Count until the bottle is empty. Use this to race or to count how many times you can hop, or jump, clap or stand up/sit down.

Dinosaurs and other small world animals

Small world farm or jungle animals, dinosaurs, etc. will engage children's interest in a way that abstract counting apparatus may not. Such collections of figures can be bought for a reasonable price at bargain shops and supermarkets. Try to have several different collections, so children have a variety to work with.

Small world collections are perfect for sorting, counting and calculating. They can also be combined with sand, water, gloop, dough and other materials to make wonderful games!

Try some maths activities outside with small world sets, and when the activity is done leave the set outside on a tray or table, or in the sand for free imaginative play.

Make simple boards or playmats with fields and paths.

Using animal sets in free play situations

Make sure the animal sets have multiples of each animal to encourage sorting, counting, grouping and sharing.

▶ Offer small world sets and environments to arrange them in. Provide fences, gates, roads, cages, trucks and transporters.

▶ Link the animal sets with construction – bricks, big blocks, inside and out.

▶ Put animal sets near water and sand trays for free use.

Numbers as labels and for counting

▶ Make a zoo, farm or other environment for the creatures. Label the cages or fields and write or add a number label to each.

▶ Sort the creatures into sets – use the children's ideas of criteria for sorting – they will often be much more imaginative!

▶ Use some number cards and a feely bag. Pick a card and take the number of creatures without peeping!

▶ Bury the creatures in sand and fish them out with nets or strainers, count your catch and find the number.

Calculating

▶ Play monster stories, e.g. there were three dinosaurs, the tyrannosaurus ate two, how many left?

▶ Play the Zoo Keeper game (see page 54). You need some small world animals and the cards on page 55. Play the game with dinosaurs for a change, and be dinosaur hunters!

▶ Put some creatures on a tray or circle of paper. Take turns to close eyes. Remove one or more of the creatures. What and how many are missing? How many left?

Shape, space and measures

▶ Use sticky paper shapes to make pictures of animals and dinosaurs. Offer squares, circles, ovals, rectangles and triangles.

▶ Play a position game with toy animals on a play mat or brick construction. Give instructions such as, 'Put the lion next to the giraffe'; 'Put the bear behind the tree'; 'Put three cows under the bridge'.

Pegs and pegboards

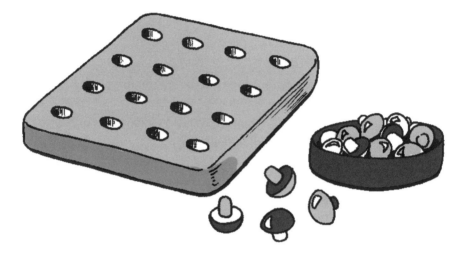

Plastic pegs and boards are another cost effective resource for maths. Try to collect different sizes and shapes of pegs and boards, and make sure that you have some boards with bigger pegs for children with less developed manual skills.

Make sure children have plenty of free play experience with this equipment before introducing structured activities. In this way they may be able to resist following their own agendas!

Keep pegs and other rolling things, such as beads, safe by using a cement mixing tray or large plastic or metal tray with a rim. Big clear plastic jars with wide tops make good storage for small items. Egg boxes and clean plastic food trays make cheap sorting boxes – for health reasons, avoid using trays from meat products.

Using pegs and boards in free play

▶ Offer pegs and boards for free choice activities. Add some cards with patterns to copy or continue.

▶ Try using the pegs in rolled out dough, plasticene or clay for children who are not ready for the boards with holes.

▶ Use pegs for sorting and grouping in sorting trays or other containers.

Numbers as labels and for counting

▶ Fill a row with pegs, then count and label.

▶ Fill rows of pegs and use to count on and back.

▶ Make a row of pegs then find the first, third, etc.

▶ Grab a handful from a bag, put in board then count.

▶ Grab a handful in the bag, guess how many, then count.

▶ Make a pattern, count the number of each colour.

▶ Throw a dice or draw a number from a bag, take the number of pegs. First to fill a row or board wins.

Calculating

▶ Throw a dice or take a card, take the number and 1, 2, 3 more.

▶ Count 1, 2, 3 or 4 pegs into a bag. Show 1, 2, 3 more and ask how many altogether.

▶ I have 0, 1, 2, 3 pegs. Give me 1, 2, 3, 4 more. How many do I have now?

▶ Put some pegs in a board. Count them. Take some out, counting back as you do so. How many now?

▶ Fill rows of pegs then count back as you remove them.

Shape, space and measures

▶ Make, continue or copy repeating patterns of colours or numbers.

▶ Sort pegs by colour, size, shape.

▶ Make the other half of a pattern.

▶ Pick a coin from a bag and put the number of pegs in your board.

▶ Use pegs to tally games, turns, register attendance, count beats of a drum, construct graphs, etc.

Magnetic numbers

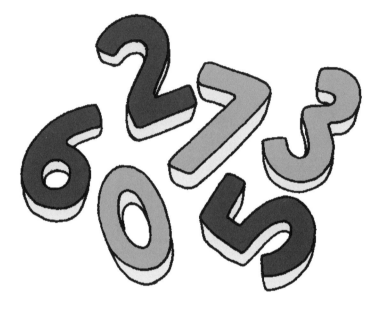

You really need several sets of these numbers, particularly for group work. You can buy sets from education suppliers or Early Learning Centres, or you can make your own from numbers with magnetic tape stuck on the back. Make the numbers from laminated card, plastic, sandpaper, baked dough or self hardening craft dough such as Fimo. Children will love helping to make these! Use a glue gun (adult only) to stick little magnets or magnetic strip on the back.

Any metal surface will work with these numbers – try trays of different sizes or baking sheets as cheap alternatives. Magnetic shapes, letters and objects are also useful – make some small fruit, vegetables, animals or people from dough bake and paint before adding magnets.

Using magnets in free play situations

▶ Magnets are fascinating to all children. Start with magnetic puzzles, shapes or pictures, so they get used to the way magnets work.

▶ Use magnet boards for calendars, name charts, weather boards.

▶ Stick magnetic strip to pictures, cards, signs and other objects.

Numbers as labels and for counting

▶ Sort and order magnetic numbers from 0 to 5 or 10.

▶ Use to score games of all sorts.

▶ Put magnetic numbers in a feely bag, put hand in and say the number before pulling it out.

▶ Take turns to take a number from a bag and order on a tin or tray. Return a number if you already have it. First to 10 wins.

▶ Order numbers 0-10 and use to count on and back.

▶ Play fishing with numbers and magnets on strings.

Calculating

▶ Take a number and stick it on a tray. Then find the number one more or one less, two more/less.

▶ Take two numbers from a bag, add and say total.

▶ Make sets of objects or shapes and combine. Label the sets.

▶ Help the children to make a magnetic nest, five magnetic eggs and five baby magnetic birds from pictures or dough. Use it to answer hatching and flying away questions. Label the nest each time with the magnetic number.

Shape, space and measures

▶ Use to record measuring activities (especially useful outside).

▶ Use with magnetic shapes to count and sort.

▶ Make magnetic shapes and objects from dough or laminated card. Stick little magnets or magnetic strip on the back and use for problem solving games. How many, sort sets etc.

Using calendars and diaries

For counting

It doesn't matter if they are out of date, calendars and diaries are excellent materials for counting on and counting back. Use felt pens to circle numbers (e.g. all the 2s). Find and circle your age, your house number, your birthday.

For ordering

Cut out numbers and days of the week for sorting and ordering. Follow the days of the week and the months of the year. Look at the number before and after. Use the months of a calendar to play 'First to Find' a number.

Time

Use calendars to help develop a sense of time. Talk about the sequence of days and months that make up the year.

Appointments

Use diaries to make appointments in role-play: hairdressers, car service, doctor's surgery, etc.

Make your own

Use calendars as models to make your own weather charts, group diaries, time lines in looking forward to events and activities. Use language such as before, after, until, next, last. Count down the days until a visit. Log visits from helpers and parents.

Regular events

Use calendars and diaries to help children keep track of time. Make daily timetables and encourage children to mark the passage of time in your setting, use the timetables to encourage children to plan their own activities and manage their own time.

Using small cars and trucks

Races and games

Line up the cars on a chalk race track or ladder and use a simple dice or spinner to make a race game. Run cars and trucks down slides and planks, mark and measure how far they go. Number the cars with little stickers for the races.

Organise them

Make a car park (with chalk or masking tape on the floor or playground). Number the spaces and organise the cars. Use simple tickets and coins to pay for parking. Sort the vehicles in colours and types. Count and label the sets of colours or types.

Through the arches

Make a simple series of arches and roll the cars through. Score on a clipboard or whiteboard

Sorting

Line up your vehicles in order of : size, type, colour, number of wheels, length.

Sets of things

Collect sets of vehicles that carry things; carry people; carry animals; deliver; dig; go off road; work in building sites; have four wheels; have more than four wheels; have flashing lights; rescue people; carry mud; work on farms; carry other vehicles; pull things; etc.

Make a Snap game

Get some toy catalogues, magazines or junk mail. Cut out or photocopy pictures of cars (or get the children to draw some vehicles of different sorts). There are some on pages 56 – 57 to copy. Make four copies of each one and use for games of Snap or Pairs.

Bingo cards

You need six bingo cards for each player. Photocopy this sheet, stick it on card and cut out to make bingo cards. You can then make all sorts of Bingo games – dotty counting, shape, number, colour or picture. You can also make money bingo by sticking plastic money or gummed coins on the cards.

Bingo boards

You need one board for each player. Photocopy and stick on card.

Coins to photocopy for games and challenges

Ladders for simple games
Copy, cut out and mount on card.

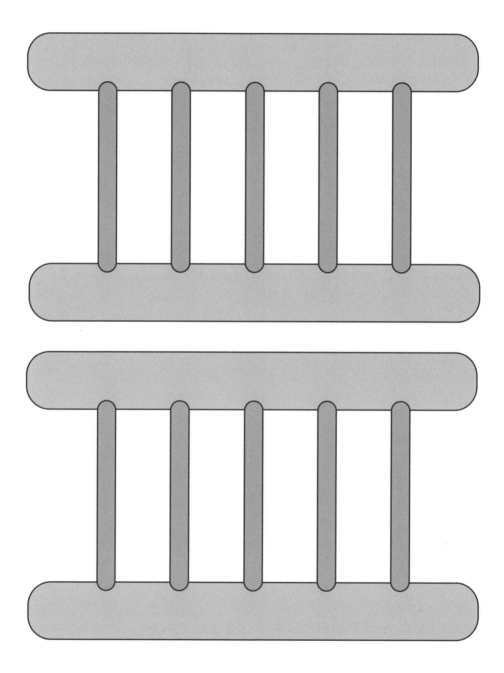

Race to the Bear's Cottage

Photocopy (enlarge to A4 or A3 if possible), put in a plastic envelope or laminate. Use the 'On 1 ', 'Back 1', 'On 2', 'Back 2' cards on the next page.

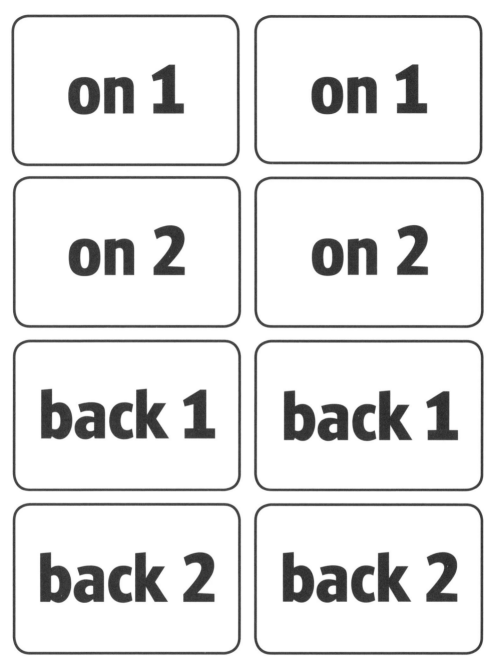

on 1	on 1
back 1	back 1
back 2	back 2

Photocopy these cards to use with the game opposite. You'll need several sets (start with 4). They'll last longer if you cover them in sticky-backed plastic (it's easier to do this before you cut them out).

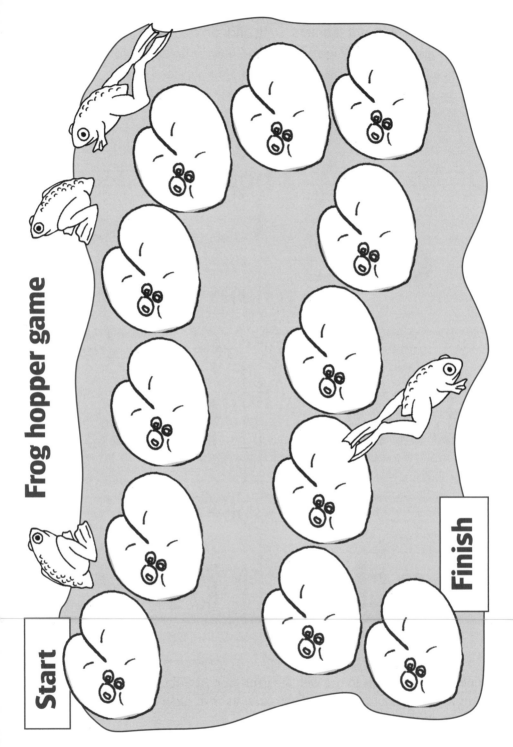

Frog hopper game

Start

Finish

52

Frog Hopper cards and counters. Copy, stick on card and cut out to play the Frog Hopper Game on Page 52. Copy the playing board (enlarge it for younger children), stick on card, colour and (if possible) laminate it.

Playing pieces – or use plastic frogs (much more fun!)

Zoo keeper game

Copy this page for each player. Copy and cut out the cards on the facing page. Collect some farm or zoo animals. Put the cards in a pile, face down on the table. Take turns to turn over a card and take or put back that number of animals. Return the card to the bottom of the pile. The winner is the first to fill their field with five/ ten animals.

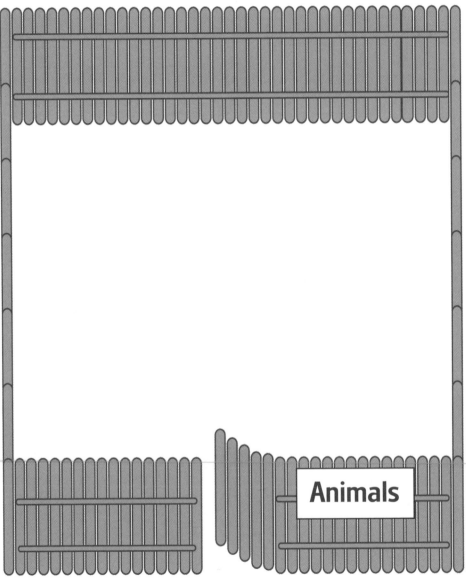

Animals

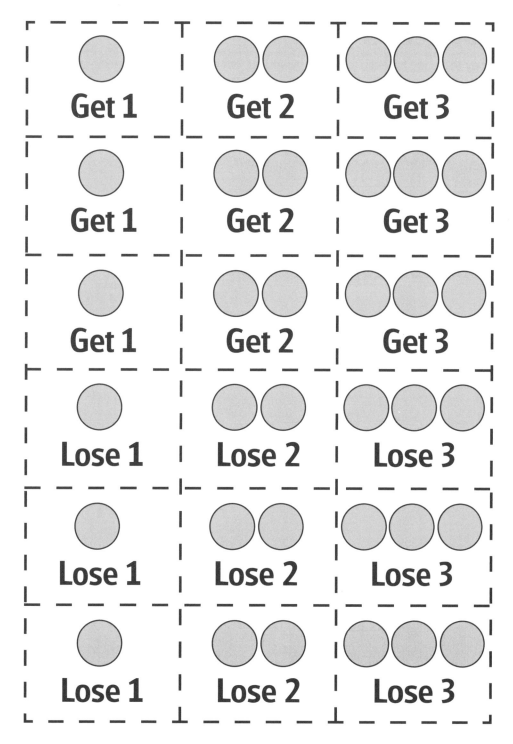

Get 1   Get 2   Get 3

Get 1   Get 2   Get 3

Get 1   Get 2   Get 3

Lose 1   Lose 2   Lose 3

Lose 1   Lose 2   Lose 3

Lose 1   Lose 2   Lose 3

Vehicle Shapes

More Vehicle Shapes

Monster race game

Game 1: Make one copy for each player. The players toss a dice and colour in the number of spots thrown. First to colour all the spots wins.

Game 2: Copy the game and stick on card or laminate. Use small toys or counters to play a race game with a dice or spinner.

(It's easier if you can enlarge the picture.)

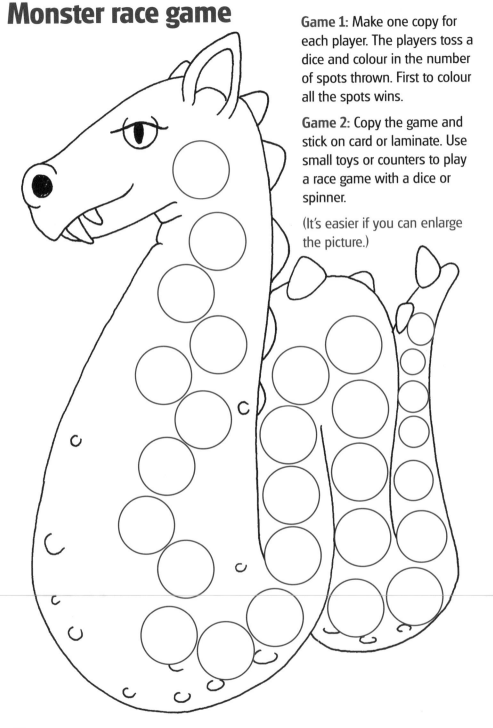

Spinners

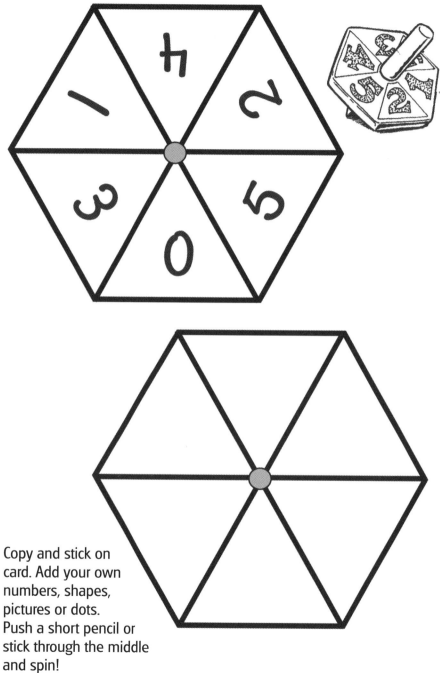

Copy and stick on card. Add your own numbers, shapes, pictures or dots. Push a short pencil or stick through the middle and spin!

Shapes

Some number rhymes and songs

For counting

▶ One, Two, Three, Four, Five, Once I Caught a Fish Alive

▶ This Little Pig went to Market

▶ Two Little Dickey Birds

▶ One Finger, One Thumb Keep Moving

For counting to 5

▶ Five Little Speckled Frogs

▶ Five Brown Buns in a Baker's Shop

▶ Five Fat Sausages

▶ Five Little Ducks went Swimming one day

▶ Peter Hammers with One Hammer

For counting to 10 and back

▶ Ten Green Bottles

▶ One Two Buckle My Shoe

▶ There were Ten in the Bed

▶ One Potato, Two Potato, Three Potato, Four

▶ One Man Went to Mow

If you have found this book useful you might also like ...

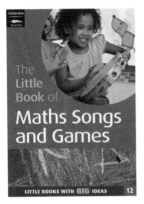

LB Maths Songs and Games
ISBN 978-1-9041-8732-5

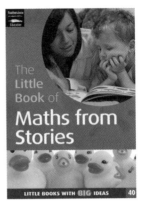

LB Maths from Stories
ISBN 978-1-9050-1925-0

LB Discovery Bottles
ISBN 978-1-9060-2971-5

LB Music
ISBN 978-1-9041-8754-7

All available from

www.acblack.com/featherstone